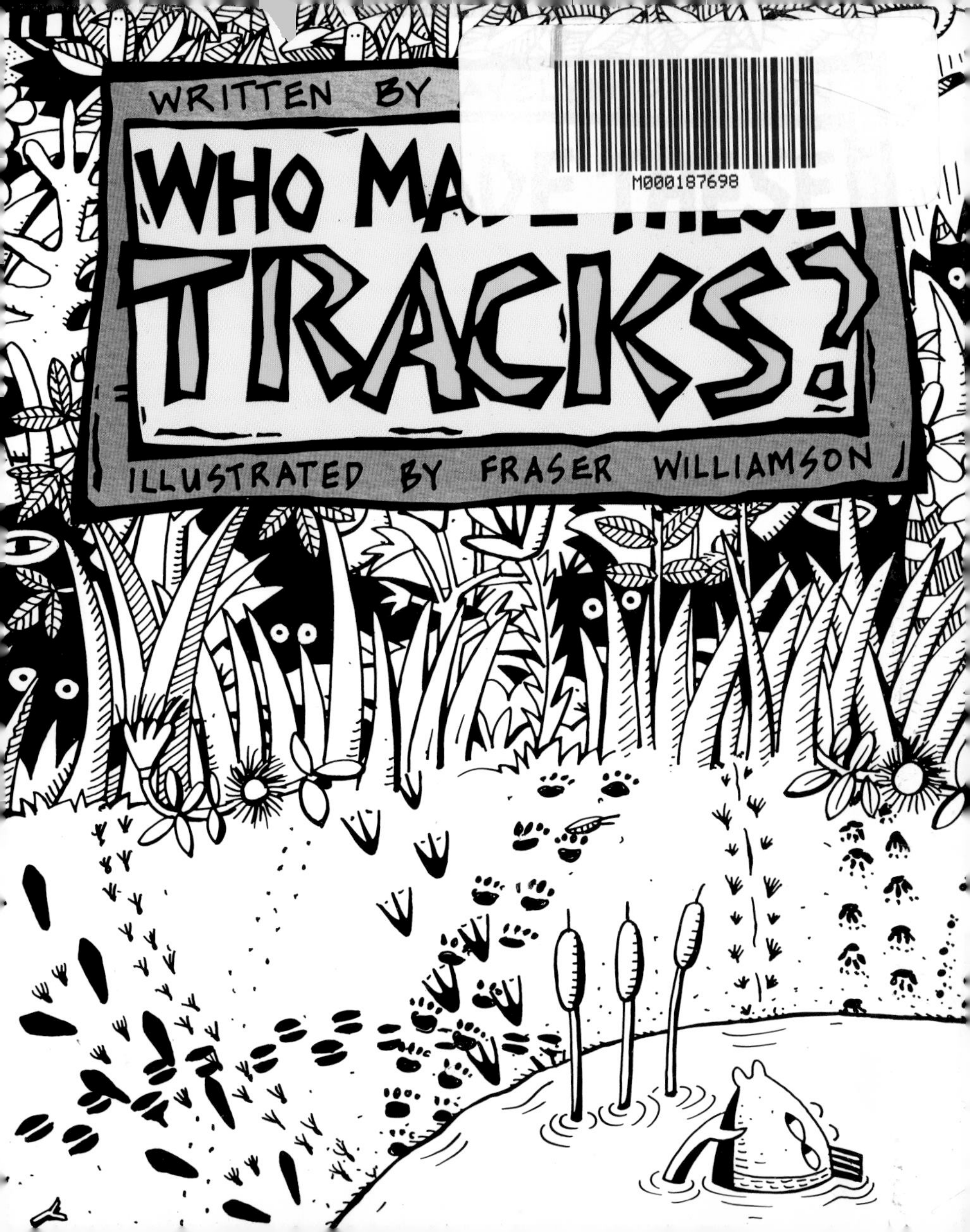

M000187698

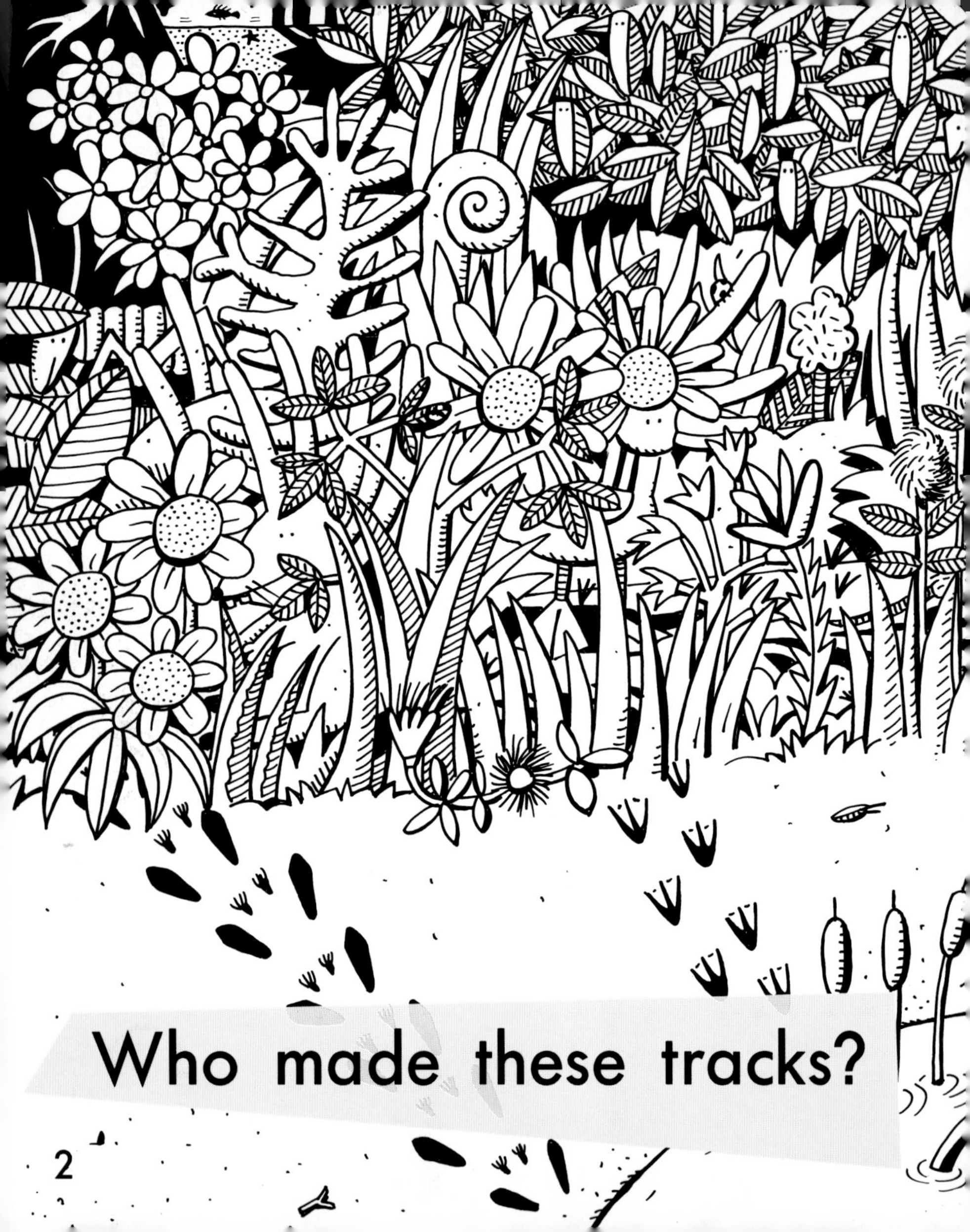

Who made these tracks?

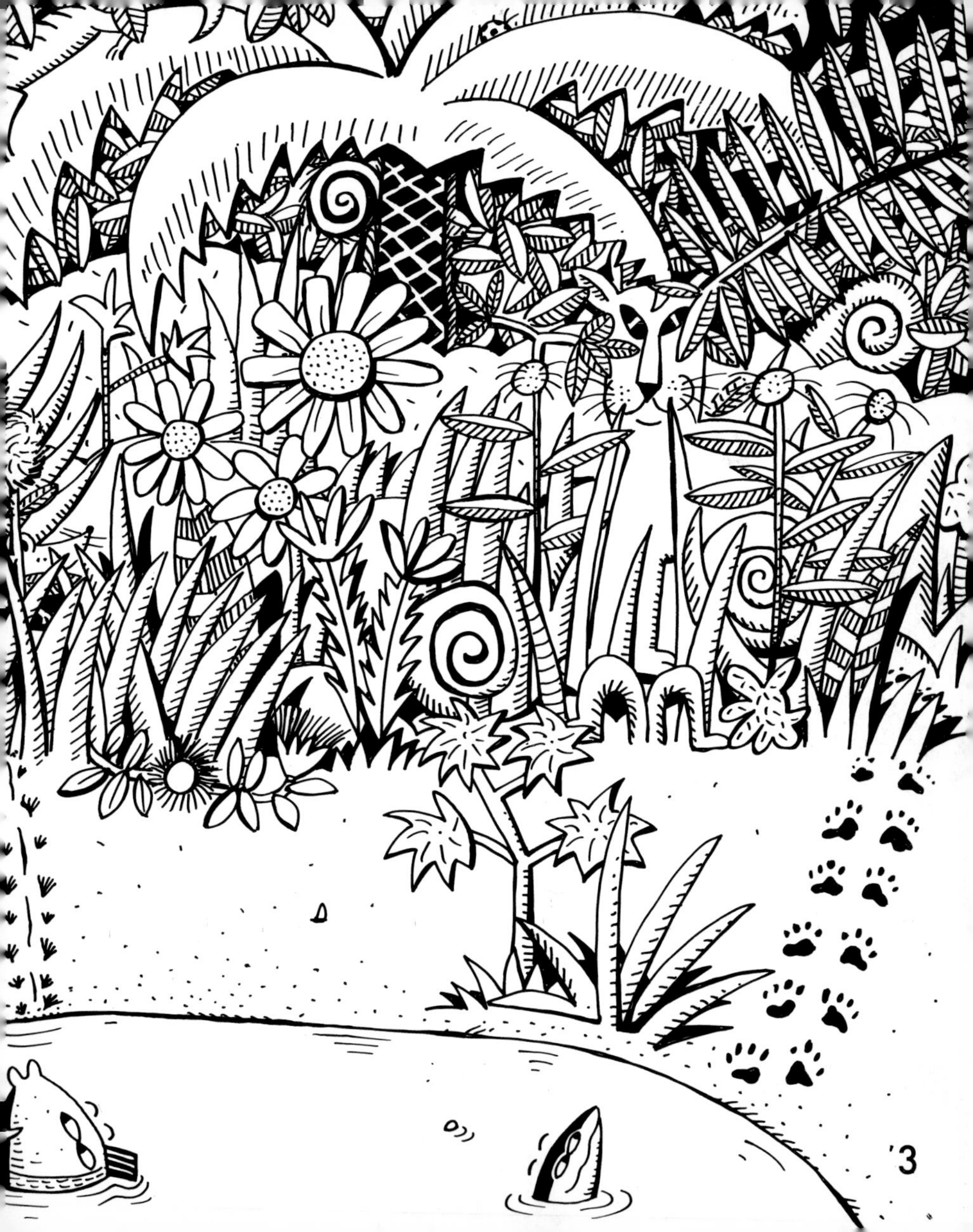

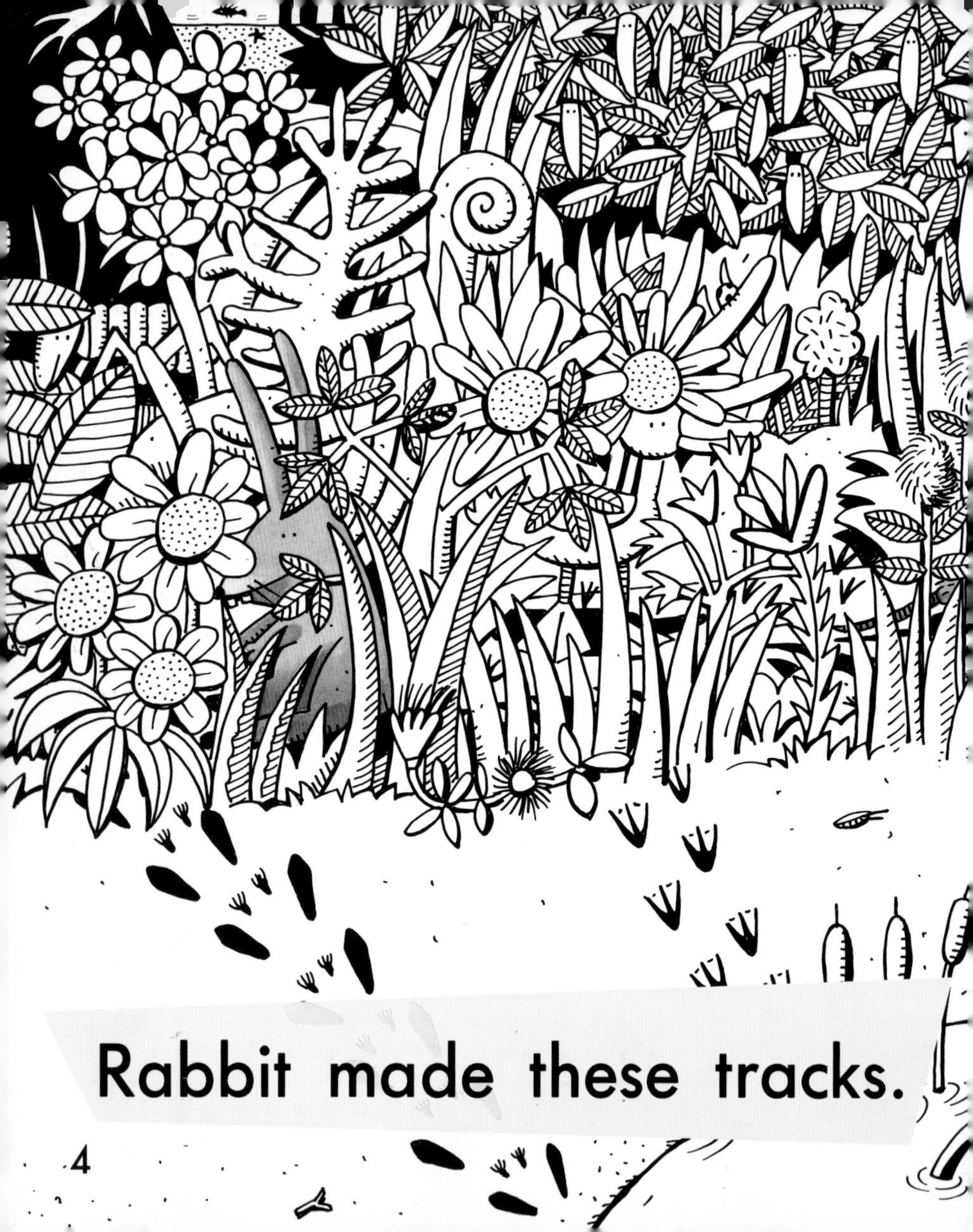

Rabbit made these tracks.

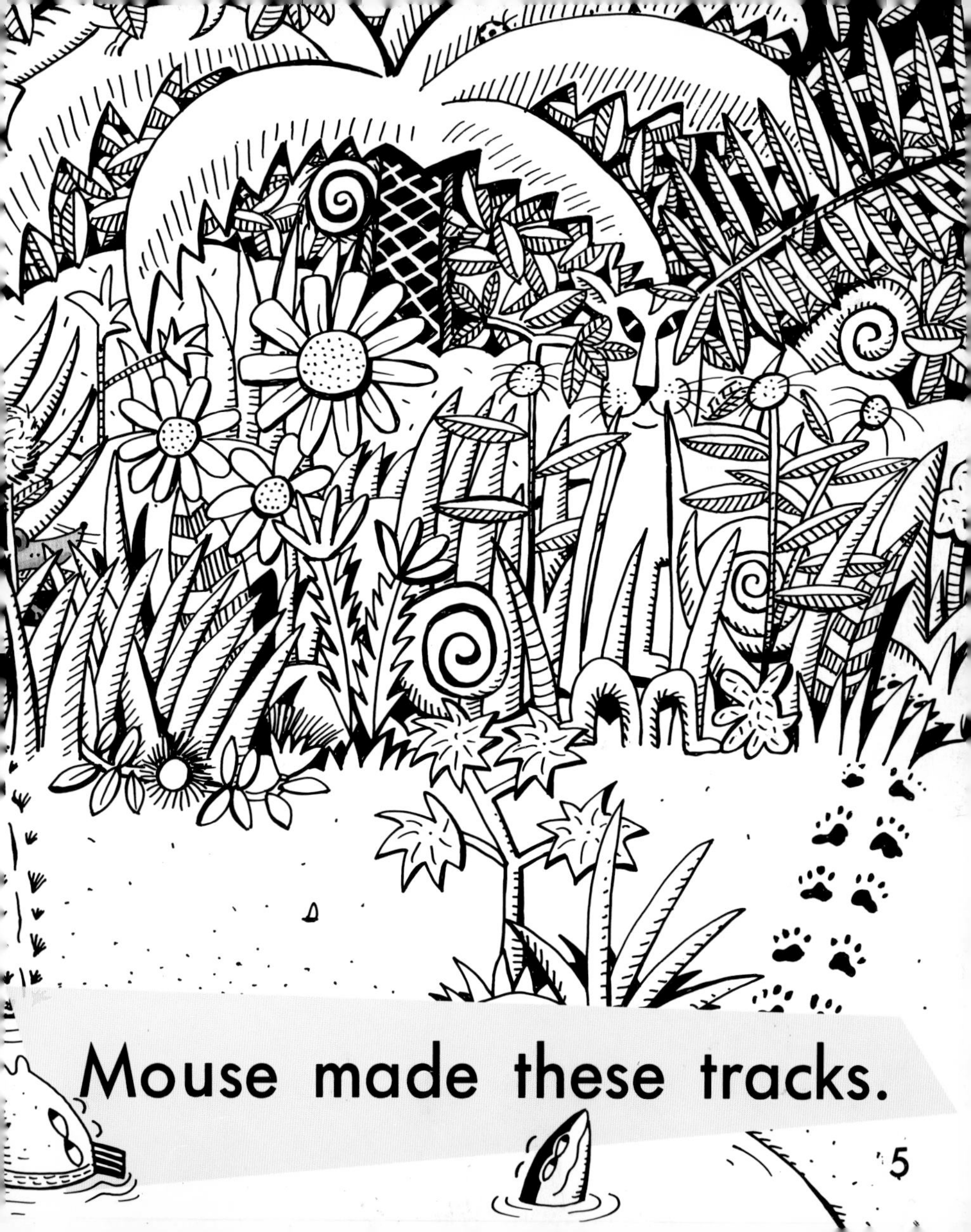

Mouse made these tracks.

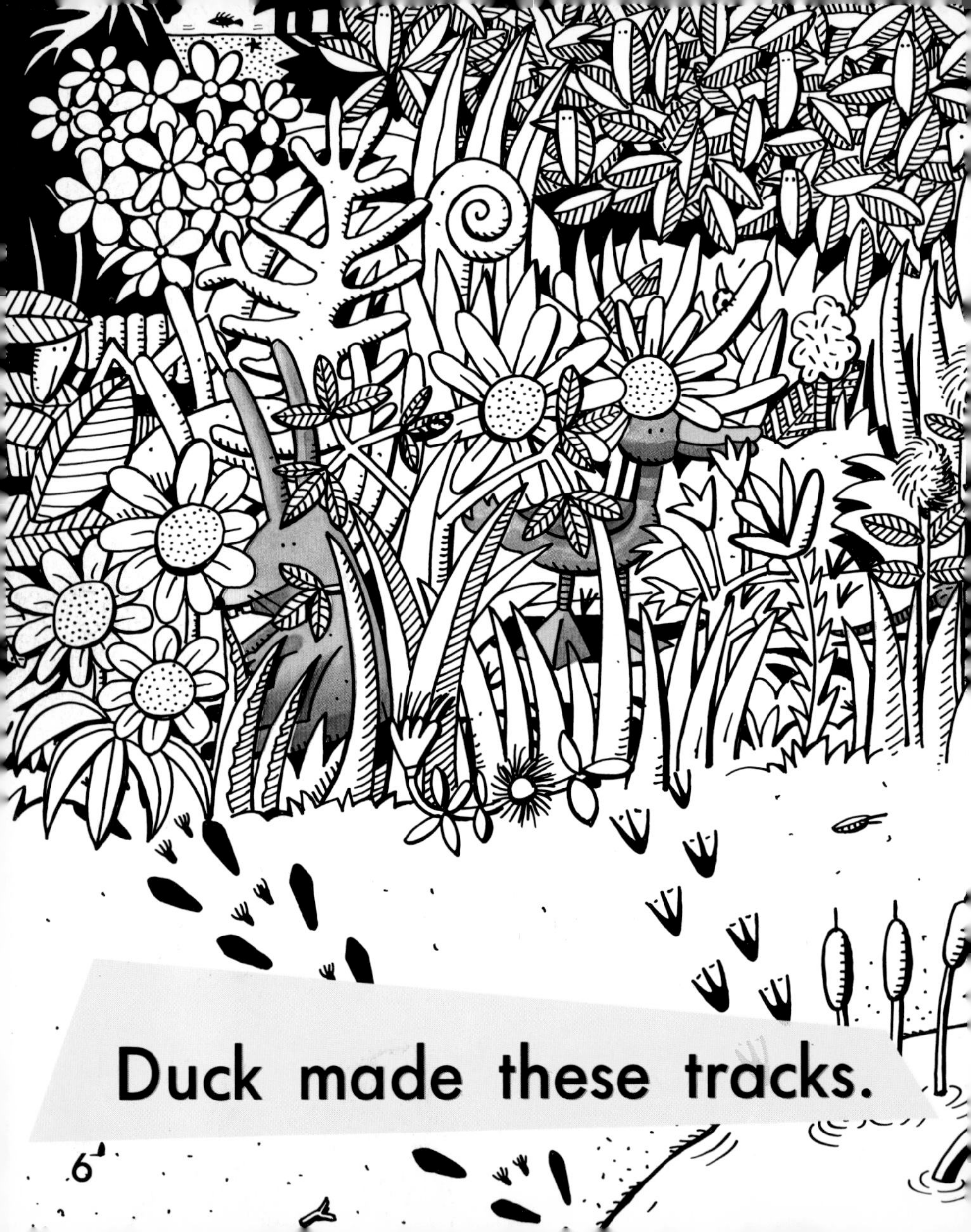

Duck made these tracks.

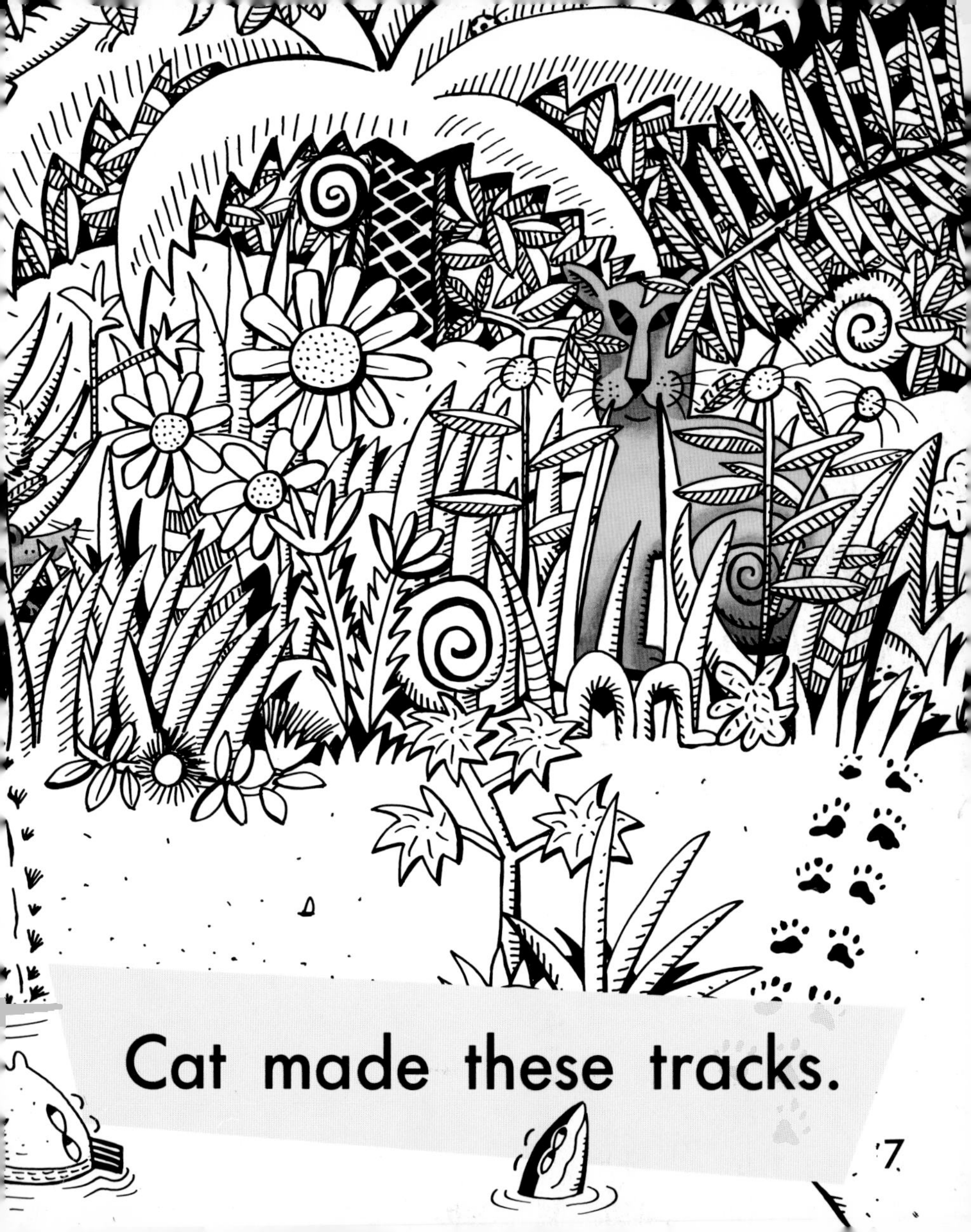

Cat made these tracks.

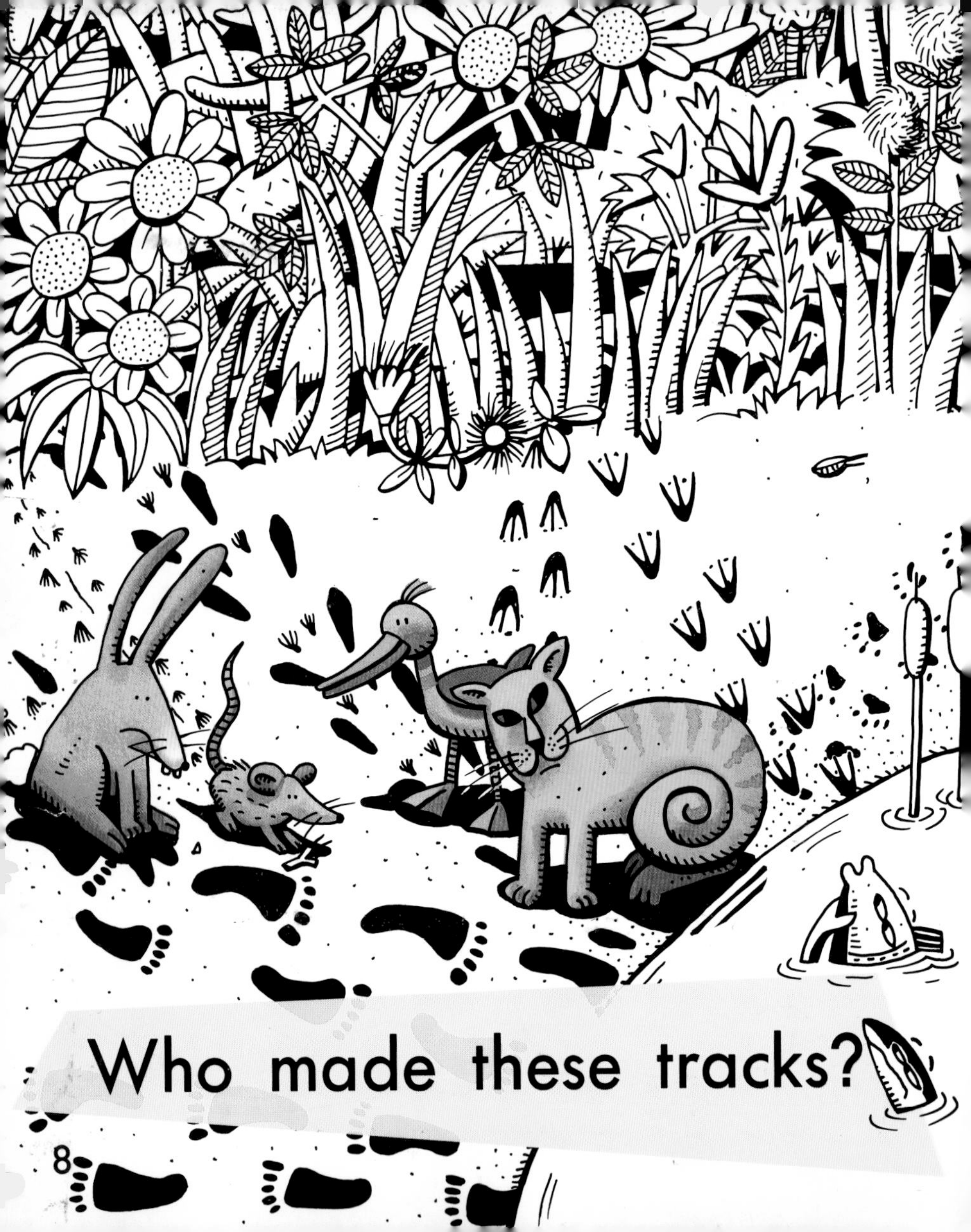

Who made these tracks?